...es belong to the Order Hymenoptera which also includes wasps, ants, sawflies and ...rasitic wasps. The life-cycle of a bee... ...m 4mm to 18mm. Bumblebees and... ...st majority of the 250 British specie... ...es some species build large numbe... ...ecies (cleptoparasites or cuckoos) d... ...her bee species, often targeting a s... ...*mada*, *Epeolus*, *Coelioxys*, *Stelis* and... ...mblebees in the genus *Bombus*, th...

Bees are important pollinators ... ...anting nectar-rich plants or by mak... ...ur garden. Bees have different methods of collecting pollen (shown right) on their ...llen brush (scopa) or pollen basket.

Finally, check if it is a bee you are ...eing — it may be a bee-fly (below left) ... a hoverfly (below right). Many ...verflies are excellent mimics of ...mblebees, honey bees and other bees. ...wever, flies have only two wings ...hereas bees have four. Flies also have ...ry short antennae.

METHODS OF CARRYING POLLEN

Megachile leafcutter bee
scopa under abdomen

Andrena mining bee
scopa on hind legs

Hylaeus
yellow-face bee
no scopa — pollen
is swallowed

Bombus bumblebee
pollen basket on hind legs

...rk-edged Bee-fly
Bombylius major

Hoverfly
Volucella bombylans

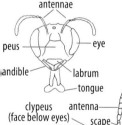

antennae

peus — eye

andible — labrum

...tongue

clypeus
(face below eyes)

...andible

BEE ANATOMY

antenna
scape
tegula
thorax
scutellar
tubercle

submarginal cells
(may be 2 or 3)

pronotal
tubercle

forewing

hindwing

propodeum

femur

T1
T2
T3
T4
T5 T6

T1–T6 = tergites
(abdominal segments)

tergite margin

abdomen (strictly the gaster)

sternites (underside)

pygidium

...erostigma

tibia
basitarsus
tarsus

Illustrations by Nick Owens

1

Bees can be found in a wide range of habitats: woodland, grassland, heathland, garden and old quarries (like these Ivy Bees *Colletes hederae* shown here at BBOWT's Dry Sandford Pit, Oxon). The main habitat and some of the best places to look locally are mentioned here (visit bbowt.org.uk/reserves for location details)

rassland and meadows

alk and limestone grasslands and the flower-rich meadows to visit are – **Berks**: Seven Barrows and
atts Bank nature reserves (all BBOWT sites); **Bucks**: Bernwood Meadows, Dancersend, Grangelands,
per Ray Meadows and Yoesden nature reserves (all BBOWT sites); **Oxon**: Chimney Meadows,
innor Hill, Dry Sandford Pit, Hartslock, Iffley Meadows, Oakley Hill, Oxey Mead, Sydlings Copse and
arburg nature reserves (all BBOWT sites), Aston Rowant National Nature Reserve and Watlington
l. **LOOK FOR** Davies' Colletes, Spined Hylaeus, Large Yellow-face Bee, Ashy Mining Bee, Yellow-
gged Mining Bee, Orange-tailed Mining Bee, Large Scabious Mining Bee, Small Scabious Mining
e, Common Mini-miner, Buffish Mining Bee, Grey-patched Mining Bee, Broad-faced Mining Bee,
ocolate Mining Bee, Wilke's Mining Bee, Orange-legged Furrow Bee, Bronze Furrow Bee, Common
rrow Bee, White-zoned Furrow Bee, Gold-tailed Melitta, Wool Carder Bee, Large Scissor Bee, Small
ssor Bee, Red-tailed Mason Bee, Welted Mason Bee, Wood-carving Leafcutter Bee, Brown-footed
afcutter Bee, Willughby's Leafcutter Bee, Fabricius' Nomad Bee, Painted Nomad Bee, Gooden's
mad Bee, Marsham's Nomad Bee, Red-tailed Bumblebee, Common Carder Bumblebee, Early
mblebee, Buff-tailed Bumblebee, Hill Cuckoo Bumblebee, Vestal Cuckoo Bumblebee, Honey Bee.

eathland

rkshire holds the vast majority of heathland in our area. **Berks**: Decoy Heath, Greenham and
okham Commons, Inkpen Common, Padworth Common, Snelsmore Common and Wildmoor Heath
l BBOWT sites); **Oxon**: Sydlings Copse (BBOWT site), North Leigh Common and Shotover Country
rk. **LOOK FOR** Large Gorse Mining Bee, Hawthorn Mining Bee, Ashy Mining Bee, Clarke's Mining
e, Yellow-legged Mining Bee, Tawny Mining Bee, Heather Mining Bee, Orange-tailed Mining Bee,
ocolate Mining Bee, Broad-margined Mining Bee, Orange-legged Furrow Bee, Bronze Furrow Bee,
hite-zoned Furrow Bee, Green Furrow Bee, Bare-saddled Blood Bee, Pantaloon Bee, Welted Mason
e, Patchwork Leafcutter Bee, Brown-footed Leafcutter Bee, Fabricius' Nomad Bee, Lathbury's
mad Bee, Early Nomad Bee, Black-horned Nomad Bee, Black-thighed Epeolus, Red-tailed
mblebee, White-tailed Bumblebee, Forest Cuckoo Bumblebee, Honey Bee.

ld quarries

on has some of the best old quarry sites to visit – Ardley Wood Quarry, Dry Sandford Pit and
tchcopse Pit nature reserves (all BBOWT sites). **LOOK FOR** Ivy Bee, Sandpit Mining Bee, Large
rse Mining Bee, Ashy Mining Bee, Yellow-legged Mining Bee, Tawny Mining Bee, Orange-tailed
ning Bee, Common Mini-miner, Buffish Mining Bee, Grey-patched Mining Bee, Orange-legged
rrow Bee, Green Furrow Bee, Bare-saddled Blood Bee, Pantaloon Bee, Red-tailed Mason Bee,
lted Mason Bee, Little Nomad Bee, Painted Nomad Bee, Hairy-footed Flower Bee, Tree Bumblebee.

Woodland

odland sites to visit are – **Berks**: Bowdown Woods and Moor Copse nature reserves (BBOWT
es), Windsor Forest; **Bucks**: Dancersend, Finemere Wood, Homefield Wood, Little Linford Wood,
shbeds Wood, Whitecross Green Wood and nature reserves (all BBOWT sites) and Bernwood
rest; **Oxon**: Foxholes, Sydlings Copse and Warburg nature reserves. **LOOK FOR** Gwynne's Mining
e, Hawthorn Mining Bee, Ashy Mining Bee, Clarke's Mining Bee, Tawny Mining Bee, Orange-tailed
ning Bee, Grey-patched Mining Bee, Small Sallow Mining Bee, Chocolate Mining Bee, Broad-
rgined Mining Bee, Orange-legged Furrow Bee, Common Furrow Bee, White-zoned Furrow Bee,
re-saddled Blood Bee, Large Scissor Bee, Red-tailed Mason Bee, Wood-carving Leafcutter Bee,
bricius' Nomad Bee, Flavous Nomad bee, Little Nomad Bee, Gooden's Nomad Bee, Early Nomad Bee,
rsham's Nomad Bee, Hairy-footed Flower Bee, Garden Bumblebee, Tree Bumblebee, Red-tailed
mblebee, White-tailed Bumblebee, Common Carder Bumblebee, Early Bumblebee, Buff-tailed
mblebee, Hill Cuckoo Bumblebee, Forest Cuckoo Bumblebee, Vestal Cuckoo Bumblebee, Honey Bee.

ardens

rdens are a haven for many bees. One of the best ways to attract them to your garden is by planting
ctar-rich flowers and buying (or making) a 'bee hotel' for hole-nesting bees. **LOOK FOR** Davies'
lletes, Common Yellow-face Bee, Hairy Yellow-face Bee, Gwynne's Mining Bee, Orange-tailed
ning Bee, Common Furrow Bee, Green Furrow Bee, Wool Carder Bee, Red Mason Bee, Blue Mason
e, Patchwork Leafcutter Bee, Wood-carving Leafcutter Bee, Brown-footed Leafcutter Bee,
lughby's Leafcutter Bee, Fabricius' Nomad Bee, Hairy-footed Flower Bee, Four-banded Flower Bee,
mmon Mourning Bee, Garden Bumblebee, Tree Bumblebee, Red-tailed Bumblebee, White-tailed
mblebee, Common Carder Bumblebee, Early Bumblebee, Buff-tailed Bumblebee, Forest Cuckoo
mblebee, Vestal Cuckoo Bumblebee, Honey Bee.

4

avies' Colletes
olletes daviesanus

ESCRIPTION Wing length: female 7mm, male 6.5mm. Females (left) have pale hairs on face, reddish-brown hairs on head and thorax and greyish-white marginal bands on abdomen. Males (below) are similar in colour.

HERE TO LOOK Flowery habitats and gardens. Visits composites (daisy family) for pollen and a wider range of flowers for nectar. Often nests in aggregations in bare/sparsely vegetated dry soils and walls with soft mortar.

HEN TO LOOK May–early September.

EPTOPARASITE Black-thighed Epeolus *Epeolus variegatus* (see p.57).

(see p.57)

IMILAR SPECIES

he rarer **Bare-saddled Colletes** *Colletes similis* is of similar size, ut has a bare first abdominal egment and prefers chalk rassland and heathland.

5

y Bee
olletes hederae

SCRIPTION Wing length: female 10mm, male 8.5mm. Females (left) are unmistakable with orange-brown hairs on thorax and orange-buff bands on abdomen. Males are similar in colour but abdominal bands are paler. Males fly low over nest sites seeking out a female to with which to mate, often large numbers of males (below) form a writhing ball around the female. Ivy Bees were first seen in Britain on the Dorset coast in 2001, reaching our area in 2011.

HERE TO LOOK Anywhere where ivy is present with nearby sandy soils and old quarries with sand and limestone cliffs, especially BBOWT's Dry Sandford Pit and Hitchcopse Pit (both Oxon) where thousands nest in aggregations. Also a sandy bank in BBOWT's Bowdown Woods (Berks).

HEN TO LOOK September–November.

EPTOPARASITE Red-thighed Epeolus *Epeolus cruciger*.

6

Common Yellow-face Bee
Hylaeus communis

DESCRIPTION Wing length: female 5mm, male 4.5mm. Females (left) have small pale yellow facial spots that hug the eye margins. Males (below) have unique facial markings.

WHERE TO LOOK A wide variety of habitats including gardens. Flowers visited include composites (daisy family), umbellifers (carrot family) and mignonettes. Will use garden 'bee hotels' in which to nest as well as hollow twigs and stems, and holes in wood, soil and walls.

WHEN TO LOOK Late May–September.

Horned Hylaeus
Hylaeus cornutus

DESCRIPTION Wing length: female 5mm, male 4.5mm. An uncommon yellow-face bee, easily recognised by its black face. Females (left and below) have two small horn-like projection on the face. Males have a unique combination of black face and mainly yellow antennae.

WHERE TO LOOK Found on umbellifer-rich grassy habitats, where it visits Wild Carrot, Wild Parsnip and Hogweed. Nests in hollow plant stems.

WHEN TO LOOK June–August.

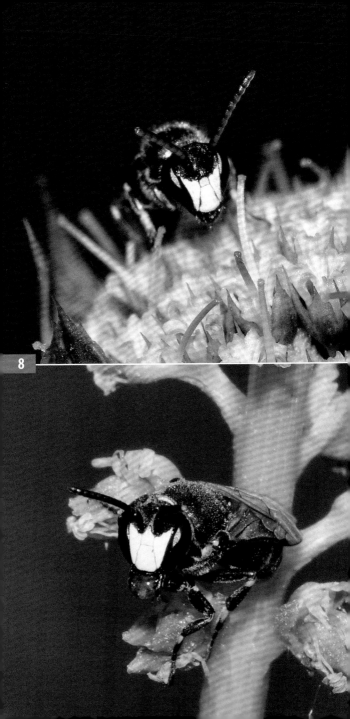

Hairy Yellow-face Bee
Hylaeus hyalinatus

look out for

DESCRIPTION Wing length: female 4.5mm, male 4.5mm. Females (below) have a long face with pale triangular facial markings. Males (left) have a white face with long white hairs. Both sexes have black antennae with orange undersides.

WHERE TO LOOK Frequently found on brownfield sites and gardens throughout the region where it visits a variety of flowers including umbellifers (daisy family), thistles and bramble. Nests in light soils and walls with soft mortar.

WHEN TO LOOK May–August.

SIMILAR SPECIES

Other yellow-face bees *Hylaeus* species are similar but have different facial markings.

Large Yellow-face Bee
Hylaeus signatus

DESCRIPTION Wing length: female 5.5mm, male 6mm. Our largest yellow-face bee and one of the few bees where the male is larger than the female. Females have small triangular facial markings. Males (left and below) have white face.

WHERE TO LOOK An uncommon bee found on chalk and limestone grassland and quarries, especially BBOWT's Dry Sandford Pit (Oxon) where it visits Wild Mignonette and Weld. Nests in hollow twigs and cliffs including old nests of Davies' Colletes (p. 5).

WHEN TO LOOK May–August.

SIMILAR SPECIES

Other yellow-face bees *Hylaeus* species are similar but have different facial markings.

Sandpit Mining Bee
Andrena barbilabris

DESCRIPTION Wing length: female 7.5mm, male 6.5mm. Females (left) have pale hairs on face, brown hair on thorax, black tibial hairs and narrow white bands on abdomen. Males (below) look fluffy with long white hairs on face, a narrow abdomen with white hair bands, and black legs.

WHERE TO LOOK Sandy soil and sand cliffs in quarries. Abundant at BBOWT's Dry Sandford Pit and Hitchcopse Pit (both Oxon) where it nests in aggregations on sloping sandy soil. Visits a variety of flowers including willows.

WHEN TO LOOK March–July.

LEPTOPARASITE Sandpit Blood Bee *Sphecodes pellucidus*.

Gwynne's Mining Bee
Andrena bicolor

look out orange hnd legs

DESCRIPTION Wing length: female 8mm, male 6mm. Females (left) have black hairs on face, red-brown hairs on thorax and abdomen, orange hair on hind femur and tibia, black hair on other leg parts. Males (below) are small and slender.

WHERE TO LOOK Common in woodland rides, scrub, waysides and gardens. Visits a variety of flowers. Spring generation uses spring blossom, dandelions, Lesser Celandine and Primrose amongst others and the summer generation uses bellflowers, composites (daisy family), bramble and others. Nests singly or in loose aggregations.

WHEN TO LOOK March–early June, mid-June–late August.

LEPTOPARASITE Fabricius' Nomad Bee *Nomada fabriciana* (see p.49).

12

Large Gorse Mining Bee
Andrena bimaculata

DESCRIPTION Wing length: female 10.5mm, male 8.5–11mm. Females (left) have mixed dark and pale facial hairs, pale hairs on thorax and tibia, and pale hair fringes on the abdomen. Some have red patches on the first two abdominal segments. Males (below) have long black hairs on face, brown hairs on thorax.

WHERE TO LOOK An uncommon bee in our region, found on heathland, sandy habitats and sandpits where there is plenty of Gorse, such as BBOWT's Hitchcopse Pit (Oxon). Spring generation visits Gorse, Blackthorn and umbellifers (daisy family), summer generation visits bramble and umbellifers. Nests in sparsely vegetated or bare ground.

WHEN TO LOOK April–June, July–August.

LEPTOPARASITE Orange-horned Nomad Bee *Nomada fulvicornis.*

Hawthorn Mining Bee
Andrena chrysosceles

DESCRIPTION Wing length: female 8.5mm, male 7.5mm. Females (below and left on top) and have pale hairs on face, narrow white bands on abdomen, reddish hind tibiae and reddish tarsi on all legs. Males (left at bottom) have a distinctive cream face with white hairs.

WHERE TO LOOK Widespread, found along woodland rides, scrubby grassland and heathland. Visits Hawthorn, willows and Cow Parsley amongst others.

WHEN TO LOOK March–June.

LEPTOPARASITE Fabricius' Nomad Bee *Nomada fabriciana* (see p.49).

SIMILAR SPECIES

There are several other similarly marked *Andrena* mining bees, but the male Hawthorn Mining Bee's face is distinctive.

Ashy Mining Bee
Andrena cineraria

✓

DESCRIPTION Wing length: female 11mm, male 10mm. Females (left) are unmistakable black bees with grey hair bands on collar and scutellum, and white hairs on face. Males (below) are narrower and similarly coloured with long white hairs on face.

WHERE TO LOOK Common and widespread, found in woodland, grassland, downland, heathland and sandy soils. Visits a wide range of spring blossoming shrubs and flowers. Nest in aggregations on bare ground.

WHEN TO LOOK April–June.

LEPTOPARASITES Lathbury's Nomad Bee *Nomada lathburiana* (see p.53) and Gooden's Nomad Bee *Nomada goodeniana* (see p.53).

Clarke's Mining Bee
Andrena clarkella

DESCRIPTION Wing length: female 11mm, male 9.5mm. Females (left) have black hairs on face, golden-brown hairs on thorax, black hairs on abdomen, hind tibia and tarsus are orange with golden-brown hairs and all other leg parts black. Males (below) are narrower and similar in colour.

WHERE TO LOOK Heathland, scrub, heathy woodland such as BBOWT's Bowdown Woods and Greenham Common (both Berks) and sandy areas. Visits flowering willows. Nests in sandy ground.

WHEN TO LOOK February–April.

LEPTOPARASITE Early Nomad Bee *Nomada leucophthalma* (see p.55).

16

Yellow-legged Mining Bee
Andrena flavipes

DESCRIPTION Wing length: female 9mm, male 9mm. Females (left) have pale and brown hairs on face, pale hairs on thorax and long yellowish pollen hairs on tibia, and broad pale marginal bands on abdomen. Males (below) are similar in colour.

WHERE TO LOOK Widespread and frequent in open habitats, chalk and limestone grassland, heathland and old quarries. Spring generation visits flowering shrubs, umbellifers (carrot family) and composites (daisy family), while the summer generation visits bramble and composites amongst others. Nests singly or in aggregations on bare or sparsely vegetated ground.

WHEN TO LOOK April–June, July–September.

CLEPTOPARASITE Painted Nomad Bee *Nomada fucata* (see p.51).

Tawny Mining Bee
Andrena fulva

DESCRIPTION Wing length: female 11mm, male 9mm. Females (left) are unmistakable and have black hair on face, sides of thorax and legs, the rest of body is a striking ginger brown. Males (below) are slender with long white hairs on face and have large mandibles, orange-brown hairs on thorax and reddish-brown marginal bands on thorax.

WHERE TO LOOK Widespread and frequent, found along woodland edges, hedgerows, scrub and heathland. Visits Blackthorn and Hawthorn blossom, Field Maple, umbellifers (carrot family), buttercups and dandelions. Nests in aggregations on footpaths, field margins, south-facing grazed grassland and flowerbeds in gardens.

WHEN TO LOOK April–June.

PARASITES Panzer's Nomad Bee *Nomada panzeri* and Broad-banded Nomad Bee *Nomada signata* (not found in our area).

18

Heather Mining Bee
Andrena fuscipes

DESCRIPTION Wing length: female 7mm, male 6.5mm. Females (left) have pale hair on face, rufous hairs on thorax, golden hairs on hind tibia and pale marginal bands on abdomen. Males (below) are slender with long pale greyish or pale brown hair and pale marginal bands on abdomen.

WHERE TO LOOK Heathland, such as BBOWT's Greenham and Crookham Commons, Decoy Heath and Wildmoor Heath (all Berks), with bare ground where it visits Heather (Ling) for nectar and pollen. Nests amongst sparse Heather.

WHEN TO LOOK Late July–September.

LEPTOPARASITE Black-horned Nomad Bee *Nomada rufipes* (see p.57).

SIMILAR SPECIES

Honey Bees *Apis mellifera* (see p.71) also visit Heather and superficially resemble female Heather Mining Bees.

Orange-tailed Mining Bee
Andrena haemorrhoa

DESCRIPTION Wing length: female 10mm, male 9.5mm. Females (left) have pale hair on face, rich red-brown hair on thorax, tibia and tarsus are orange-red with golden hair on hind tibia, abdomen has whitish hair and a tuft of reddish hairs at the tip. Males (below) are similar.

WHERE TO LOOK Common and widespread in most habitats. Visits spring blossoming shrubs, willows and Gorse and many different flowers. Nests singly or in loose aggregations.

WHEN TO LOOK Late March–June.

LEPTOPARASITE Fork-jawed Nomad Bee *Nomada ruficornis*.

SIMILAR SPECIES

Grey-patched Mining Bee *Andrena nitida* (see p.25) is slightly larger (wing length: female 12mm).

Large Scabious Mining Bee
Andrena hattorfiana

DESCRIPTION Wing length: female 12mm, male 10.5mm. Females (left and below) have white hairs on face and thorax, tibia hairs are yellowish above and white below (unmistakable when covered in pink pollen from scabious flowers), abdomen is black or partly red, wings are suffused with brown. Males are similar in colour.

WHERE TO LOOK Rare, found in scabious-rich habitats, downland and limestone grassland such as BBOWT's Dry Sandford Pit (Oxon). Visits Field Scabious and sometimes Small Scabious. Nest in bare ground and very short turf.

WHEN TO LOOK Late June–August.

CLEPTOPARASITE Armed Nomad Bee *Nomada armata* (not found in our region).

Small Scabious Mining Bee
Andrena marginata

DESCRIPTION Wing length: female 7.5mm, male 6mm. Females (left and below) have whitish hair on face and thorax, pale hairs on hind tibia which, like the Large Scabious Mining Bee (above), can be covered in pink pollen from scabious flowers. Abdomen has variable amounts of orange with white marginal bands. Males have a white face but are otherwise black.

WHERE TO LOOK Rare in scabious-rich chalk downland such as BBOWT's Hartslock reserve (Oxon), where it visits Field Scabious and Small Scabious. Nests in light soils in bare ground and short turf.

WHEN TO LOOK July–September.

CLEPTOPARASITE Silver-sided Nomad Bee *Nomada argentata* (not found in our area).

Common Mini-miner
Andrena minutula

DESCRIPTION Wing length: female 5.5mm, male 5mm. A small blackish bee, females (left) have yellowish-white body hairs, Males (below) are similar but more slender.

WHERE TO LOOK Widespread, found in a wide variety of habitats. Spring generation visits flowering shrubs, willows, Colt's-foot, dandelions and Daisy, whilst the summer generation visits umbellifers (carrot family) and composites (daisy family). Nests in dry soils.

WHEN TO LOOK Mid-March–May, June–September.

CLEPTOPARASITE Little Nomad Bee *Nomada flavoguttata* (see p.51).

SIMILAR SPECIES

The less common **Shiny-margined Mini-miner** *Andrena semilaevis* and **Impunctate Mini-miner** *Andrena subopaca*.

Buffish Mining Bee
Andrena nigroaenea

DESCRIPTION Wing length: female 10.5mm, male 10mm. Females (left and below) have black and brown hairs on face, ginger brown hairs on thorax and bright ginger hairs on the hind femur and tibia. Abdomen has a covering of short ginger hairs with black hairs at tip. Males are similar.

WHERE TO LOOK Common and widespread, found in a wide variety of habitats. Visits flowering shrubs, composites (daisy family), umbellifers (carrot family) and buttercups amongst others. Nests in bare ground, short-cropped grass and in walls with soft mortar.

WHEN TO LOOK March–June.

CLEPTOPARASITES Gooden's Nomad Bee *Nomada goodeniana* (see p.53) and Marsham's Nomad Bee *Nomada marshamella* (see p.55).

24

Grey-patched Mining Bee
Andrena nitida

DESCRIPTION Wing length: female 12mm, male 10mm. Females (left) have pale hairs on face with black hairs around the antennae, red-brown hair on thorax grading to white beneath, hind tibia have dark hairs above and white below, abdomen has white hair tufts on the sides. Males (below) are narrower and similar in colour.

WHERE TO LOOK Widespread, found in a wide variety of habitats with fairly dry soils. Good BBOWT sites to see it are Dry Sandford Pit (Oxon), Yoesden (Bucks) and Bowdown Woods (Berks). Visits spring-flowering shrubs, also umbellifers (carrot family), composites (daisy family) and Wood Spurge. Nests in flat or sloping turf.

WHEN TO LOOK April–June.

CLEPTOPARASITE Gooden's Nomad Bee *Nomada goodeniana* (see p.53).

SIMILAR SPECIES
Orange-tailed Mining Bee *Andrena haemorrhoa* (see p.19) has an orange-tipped abdomen.

Small Sallow Mining Bee
Andrena praecox

DESCRIPTION Wing length: female 9.5mm, male 8.5mm. Females (left) have pale hairs on face with dark hairs along eye margins, orange-brown hairs on upper thorax grading to long pale hairs below the wings, tibia hairs are pale above and dark below, long pale brown hairs on the first two abdominal segments. Males (below) have long antennae, long mandibles and pale hairs on face.

WHERE TO LOOK Widespread, found in willow-rich habitats. Visits a wide range of willow species. Nests in light soils.

WHEN TO LOOK March–May.

CLEPTOPARASITE Yellow-shouldered Nomad Bee *Nomada ferruginata*.

SIMILAR SPECIES
Large Sallow Mining Bee *Andrena apicata* is larger with a wing length of 10.5mm in female and 9mm in male.

26

Broad-faced Mining Bee
Andrena proxima

DESCRIPTION Wing length: female 8.5mm, male 7.5mm. Females (left and below) are slender with inconspicuous brown hairs on thorax. Abdomen is shiny and bare, with white bands on the sides of abdominal segments two to four. Males are similar but narrower.

WHERE TO LOOK A scarce southern bee found on chalk grassland with plenty of umbellifers (carrot family). Rare in our region, where it has been recorded mainly from the Chilterns at sites such as BBOWT's Grangelands reserve (Bucks). Visits a range of umbellifer species. Nests in very short turf.

WHEN TO LOOK May–July.

CLEPTOPARASITE Fringeless Nomad Bee *Nomada conjungens* (not found in our area).

Chocolate Mining Bee
Andrena scotica

DESCRIPTION Wing length: female 10.5mm, male 9.5mm. Females (left and below) have brown and black hairs on face, pale brown hair on thorax and a covering of fine brown hairs on the abdomen, hind tibia has black hairs above and white below. Males are similar. This is the most often parasitised mining bee by *Stylops* species (two are shown in the left-hand picture poking out from the abdomen).

WHERE TO LOOK Common and widespread, found in a variety of habitats. Visits a wide range of flowering shrubs, umbellifers (carrot family) and composites (daisy family). Nests singly or in loose aggregations, often amongst vegetation and leaf litter.

WHEN TO LOOK Mid-March–July.

CLEPTOPARASITES Flavous Nomad Bee *Nomada flava* (see p.49), Marsham's Nomad Bee *Nomada marshamella* (see p.55).

28

Broad-margined Mining Bee
Andrena synadelpha

DESCRIPTION Wing length: female 9.5mm, male 7.5mm. Females (left) have dark hairs on face, reddish-brown hairs on thorax, reddish-brown hairs on abdomen but black hairs on tip, hind tibia had dark hairs above and pale below. Males (below) have pale hair on face, long antennae and long mandibles.

WHERE TO LOOK Woodland rides, especially heathy woodland, such as those at BBOWT's Bowdown Woods (Berks) and heathland.
Visits flowering shrubs, umbellifers (carrot family), Wood Spurge and dandelions. Nests singly or in loose aggregations.

WHEN TO LOOK April–June.

CLEPTOPARASITE Panzer's Nomad Bee *Nomada panzeri*.

Wilke's Mining Bee
Andrena wilkella

DESCRIPTION Wing length: female 8mm, male 8mm. Females (left and below) have grey-brown hairs on face and thorax, pale hairs on tibia, white marginal bands on abdomen, narrowing towards centre leaving a clear gap on first two abdominal segments, orange hairs on tip of abdomen. Hind tibia and tarsus are orange. Males are similar.

WHERE TO LOOK Widespread, found on legume-rich grasslands.
Visits clovers, bird's-foot-trefoils, vetches, melilots, gorse and broom. Nests singly or in loose aggregations.

WHEN TO LOOK April–early July.

CLEPTOPARASITE Blunt-jawed Nomad Bee *Nomada striata*.

Orange-legged Furrow Bee
Halictus rubicundus

DESCRIPTION Wing length: female 8mm, male 7.5mm. Females (left and below) have red hair on head and thorax, orange legs and white marginal bands on the abdomen, the tip of which is grooved (furrowed). Males are similar but slimmer with long antennae and yellower legs.

WHERE TO LOOK Widespread, found on a wide range of habitats. Visits composites (daisy family) and umbellifers (carrot family). Nests in light soils, sometimes in large aggregations.

WHEN TO LOOK March–October, males from mid-June.

CLEPTOPARASITES Dark-winged Blood Bee *Sphecodes gibbus* and Box-headed Blood Bee *Sphecodes monilicornis*.

SIMILAR SPECIES

White-zoned Furrow Bee
Lasioglossum leucozonium
(see p.33) is smaller and has
black legs.

Bronze Furrow Bee
Halictus tumulorum

DESCRIPTION Wing length: female 5.5mm, male 5.5mm. Females (left) have a dull greenish sheen, abdomen has dull white margins to the sections and a grooved tip. Males (below) are also metallic green, have very long antennae and all legs are mostly yellow.

WHERE TO LOOK Widespread and common, found on open habitats including grasslands and heathlands. Visits spring-flowering trees and shrubs such as willows and Blackthorn, and a wide variety of flowers. Nests in light soils.

WHEN TO LOOK March–October, males from late-June.

CLEPTOPARASITE Bare-saddled Blood Bee *Sphecodes ephippius* (see p.35).

Common Furrow Bee
Lasioglossum calceatum

DESCRIPTION Wing length: female 7mm, male 7mm. Females (left) have a round face, pale rust-brown body hairs, white hair patches on the margins of abdominal sections which are transparent making them look orange. Males (below) are slim with dark antennae, pale tarsi and ends of tibiae, some have red on the abdomen.

WHERE TO LOOK Common and widespread. Found on a wide variety of habitats. Visits many types of flowers including spring-flowering shrubs. Males often seen on composites (daisy family) and scabiouses. Nests singly or in small aggregations.

WHEN TO LOOK April–September, males from June.

CLEPTOPARASITE Box-headed Blood Bee *Sphecodes monilicornis*.

SIMILAR SPECIES

Bloomed Furrow Bee *Lasioglossum albipes* has a longer face, is slightly smaller, but otherwise virtually identical in appearance.

White-zoned Furrow Bee
Lasioglossum leucozonium

DESCRIPTION Wing length: female 6.5mm, male 6mm. Females (left and below) are robust with a round face, a dull-looking thorax and bold white hair bands on abdomen. Males are similar.

WHERE TO LOOK Common and widespread in a variety of habitats, preferring lighter soils, heathland and sandy areas. Visits composites (daisy family). Nests singly on south-facing slopes and along sandy paths.

WHEN TO LOOK May–September, males from late June.

CLEPTOPARASITE Bare-saddled Blood Bee *Sphecodes ephippius* (see p.35).

34

Green Furrow Bee
Lasioglossum morio

DESCRIPTION Wing length: female 4mm, male 4mm. Females (left) are dull metallic green and slim with a long face and hair bands on the abdomen. Males (below) are slender with very long antennae and have dark legs.

WHERE TO LOOK Common and widespread in a wide variety of habitats, including gardens. Visits composites (daisy family), flowering shrubs and many others, including cultivated flowers. Nests in south-facing slopes and walls, usually in large aggregations.

WHEN TO LOOK March–October, males from June.

CLEPTOPARASITE Dark Blood Bee *Sphecodes niger*.

SIMILAR SPECIES

Their are three other *Lasioglossum* furrow bees with a metallic sheen.

Bare-saddled Blood Bee
Sphecodes ephippius

DESCRIPTION Wing length: female 6.5mm, male 5mm. Females (left and below) have moderately dense punctures on the thorax and red on abdomen extends to the fourth abdominal segment. Males are similar.

WHERE TO LOOK Found on a wide range of habitats including heathland, old quarries, grassland and woodland rides such as BBOWT's Dry Sandford Pit (Oxon), Whitecross Green Wood (Bucks) and Bowdown Woods (Berks). Visits composites especially dandelions in the spring. A cleptoparasite, the female lays her eggs in nests of the Bronze Furrow Bee *Halictus tumulorum* (see p.31) and White-zoned Furrow Bee *Lasioglossum leucozonium* (see p.33).

WHEN TO LOOK April–September, males from July.

SIMILAR SPECIES

Sandpit Blood Bee *Sphecodes pellucidus* and other *Sphecodes* species.

36

Gold-tailed Melitta
Melitta haemorrhoidalis

DESCRIPTION Wing length: female 8.5mm, male 8mm. Females (left and below) have pale hair on face, pale orange and dark hairs on thorax, fine marginal bands on abdominal segments and orange hair on the tip of the abdomen. Males are similar but hairier with more obvious hair bands on abdomen.

WHERE TO LOOK Chalk downland and grasslands, mainly in the Chilterns and Berkshire Downs. Visits Harebell and Clustered Bellflower. Nesting has not been observed.

WHEN TO LOOK July–September.

SIMILAR SPECIES

The much rarer **Red Bartsia Bee *Melitta tricincta*** doesn't have the orange-tipped abdomen. It visits Red Bartsia flowers in chalk and limestone grassland in late summer.

Pantaloon Bee
Dasypoda hirtipes

DESCRIPTION Wing length: female 11mm, male 11mm. Females (left and below) are unmistakable with very long hairs on the hind tibia, which when covered in pollen resemble pantaloons. They have pale hairs on the face and a ruff of pale hairs around the back and sides of the head, orange and black hairs on thorax and prominent white marginal hair bands on the abdomen. Males are a more uniform orange-brown, fading to grey over time.

WHERE TO LOOK Rare in our area where it is occasionally found on sandy sites such as BBOWT's Dry Sandford Pit (Oxon) and heathland. Visits yellow composites (daisy family). Nests in sandy ground.

WHEN TO LOOK Mid-June–August.

Wool Carder Bee
Anthidium manicatum

DESCRIPTION Wing length: female 10mm, male 12mm. Females (left) have a row of yellow spots (sometimes bars) along the abdomen, the scopa hairs (beneath the abdomen) are white. The larger males (below) are similarly marked and have a row of spines at the end of the abdomen which they use to fend off other insects straying into their territory.

WHERE TO LOOK Most often seen in gardens where labiates such as Lamb's-ear is grown, but can be found on a variety of habitats. Visits woundworts, Black Horehound and Lamb's-ear, females also visit vetches and trefoils. Nests in cavities in walls, dead wood and hollow stems. The nest's cell walls and closing plug are made from hairs gathered by the females from plants with furry leaves.

WHEN TO LOOK Late May–August.

CLEPTOPARASITE Banded Dark Bee *Stelis punctulatissima*.

Large Scissor Bee
Chelostoma florisomne

DESCRIPTION Wing length: female 8mm, male 8mm. Females (left and below) have long, curved mandibles, white hairs on the body and scopa, and white marginal hair bands. Males are similar.

WHERE TO LOOK Rare in our area where it is found in meadows and woodland rides. Visits buttercups. Nests in holes on dead wood, hollow stem, building timber and in 'bee hotels'.

WHEN TO LOOK May–July.

CLEPTOPARASITE The club-horned wasp *Monosapyga clavicornis*.

SIMILAR SPECIES

Small Scissor Bee *Chelostoma campanularum*, Britain's smallest bee, with a wing length of 4mm visits Harebell and other bellflowers.

40

Red-tailed Mason Bee
Osmia bicolor

DESCRIPTION Wing length: female 8mm, male 7.5mm. Females (left) have black hair on the head and thorax, orange-red hairs on the abdomen and scopa. Males (below) have pale hairs on face and buff-brown hairs on most of the body.

WHERE TO LOOK Chalk and limestone grassland, woodland rides in chalk and limestone areas and old quarries. Visits spring-flowering trees and shrubs, vetches and trefoils, Bugle, Ground-ivy, dead-nettles, Wood Spurge and composites (daisy family). Nest is empty snail shells, especially those of White-lipped and Brown-lipped Snails. The female then covers the shell with pieces of grass and dead leaves. This fascinating bee can be seen at several BBOWT nature reserves such as Dry Sandford Pit and Warburg Reserve (both Oxon), Grangelands and Yoesden (both Bucks).

WHEN TO LOOK March–June.

Red Mason Bee
Osmia bicornis

DESCRIPTION Wing length: female 10mm, male 8mm. Females (left) have pale hair on face, black hair on top of the head, pale hairs on thorax and orange hair on abdomen and scopa. Males (below) have long antennae and are similar in colour but with less black hair on the head.

WHERE TO LOOK Our most common mason bee, found in a variety of habitats but is often seen in gardens, churchyards and urban greenspace. Visits spring-flowering shrubs and a wide variety of wild and garden flowers, an important pollinator of fruit trees and Oil-seed Rape. Nests in holes in walls, hollow stems and sandy banks.

WHEN TO LOOK March–July.

CLEPTOPARASITE The club-horned wasp *Sapyga quinquepunctata*.

42

Blue Mason Bee
Osmia caerulescens

DESCRIPTION Wing length: female 8.5mm, male 6mm. Females (left) have a large, square head, black body with slightly blueish reflection, white hair bands on the abdomen and black scopa hairs. Males (below) are very different and slightly metallic with orange hair on head, thorax and abdomen.

WHERE TO LOOK Found in a variety of habitats but is often seen in gardens, churchyards, parks and other urban areas. Visits trefoils, clovers, Ivy-leaved Toadflax, Ground-ivy, woundworts, lavenders, speedwells, and composites (daisy family). Nests in holes and cavities in old mortar of walls, fence posts and hollow stems.

WHEN TO LOOK Late April–July.

CLEPTOPARASITE The club-horned wasp *Sapyga quinquepunctata*.

Welted Mason Bee
Hoplitis claviventris

DESCRIPTION Wing length: female 6mm, male 6mm. Females (left and below) have black head and body with pale brown hairs on face and upper thorax, long white hairs beneath wings, white marginal bands on abdomen and pale hairs on scopa. Males are similar but have greenish eyes.

WHERE TO LOOK Uncommon in our area where it is found on grasslands, old quarries and heathland. Visits bird's-foot-trefoils mainly. Nests in hollow twigs and stems.

WHEN TO LOOK May–September.

CLEPTOPARASITE Spotted Dark Bee *Stelis ornatula*.

SIMILAR SPECIES

Female is superficially similar to female **Blue-mason Bee *Osmia caerulescens*** (above) but scopa is black in Blue Mason Bee but pale in Welted Mason Bee.

Patchwork Leafcutter Bee
Megachile centuncularis

DESCRIPTION Wing length: female 8.5mm, male 8mm. Females (left and below) have pale hairs on face and thorax, pale marginal bands at edges of abdominal segments and orange scopa hairs. Males have pale hairs on face, a mixture of pale and dark hairs on top of head and thorax and pale marginal bands.

WHERE TO LOOK Widespread and fairly common in gardens, waysides, heathland. Visits composites (daisy family), bird's-foot-trefoils, brambles and St John's-worts. Nests in dead wood, cavities in walls, 'bee hotels' where it uses leaves (cut with its scissor-like mandibles) of roses and a variety of other plants.

WHEN TO LOOK June–August.

CLEPTOPARASITE Shiny-vented Sharp-tail Bee *Coelioxys inermis*.

Wood-carving Leafcutter Bee
Megachile ligniseca

DESCRIPTION Wing length: female 12mm, male 11mm. Females (left and below) have pale brown hair on face and thorax, black hair on top of head, pale marginal bands on abdomen and the scopa hairs are white grading to pale orange at the back. Males have pale hairs on face, pale brown hairs on top of head and thorax, and pale marginal bands on a parallel-sided abdomen.

WHERE TO LOOK Found in a variety of habitats including gardens. Visits thistles, burdocks, knapweeds and brambles and Field Scabious. Nests in dead wood, tree stumps, log piles, old fence posts and 'bee hotels'.

WHEN TO LOOK June–September.

Brown-footed Leafcutter Bee
Megachile versicolor

DESCRIPTION Wing length: female 9mm, male 8.5mm. Females (left) are similar in appearance to Patchwork Leafcutter Bees *Megachile centrunculus* (see p.45), but the marginal bands on the abdomen are less prominent and the scopa hairs are orange with black hairs to the rear. Males (below) are also similar in appearance to Patchwork Leafcutter Bees.

WHERE TO LOOK Widespread and found in flowery grassland, heathland and gardens. Visits composites (daisy family), trefoils, vetches and brambles. Nests in dead wood and hollow thistle stems, using rose leaves for nest building.

WHEN TO LOOK Late May–early September.

CLEPTOPARASITE Shiny-vented Sharp-tail Bee *Coelioxys inermis*.

Willughby's Leafcutter Bee
Megachile willughbiella

DESCRIPTION Wing length: female 10.5mm, male 9mm. Females (below) are broad with brownish hair and scopa is pale orange with black hairs along the edge at the rear. Males (left) have ginger hair on upper body and greatly expanded whitish front tarsi.

WHERE TO LOOK Widespread and frequent in gardens and a wide variety of habitats. Visits bird's-foot-trefoils and other legumes, composites (daisy family), bramble, bellflowers and willowherbs. Nests in dead wood, holes in walls and a variety of artificial cavities in gardens, including 'bee hotels'. Uses a variety of leaves for nests from trees, shrubs and herbaceous plants.

WHEN TO LOOK Late May–August.

CLEPTOPARASITES Sharp-tail bees *Coelioxys* species.

48

Fabricius' Nomad Bee
Nomada fabriciana

DESCRIPTION Wing length: female 8mm, male 7mm. Females (left) have black and
orange antennae, a largely black head and thorax, and the abdomen red with a
yellow spot at the side, but this can be absent in some. Males (below) are similar
but have dark antennae.

WHERE TO LOOK Found in a variety of open and wooded habitats including gardens.
Visits flowering shrubs, dandelions, buttercups, Primrose
and Garlic Mustard in spring, ragworts, thistles and
scabiouses in summer. A cleptoparasite, the
female lays her eggs in the nests of
Gwynne's Mining Bee *Andrena bicolor*
(see p.11) and Hawthorn Mining Bee
Andrena chrysosceles (see p.13).

WHEN TO LOOK March–June,
June–August.

SIMILAR SPECIES

**Yellow-shouldered Nomad
Bee *Nomada ferruginata*** and
other nomads with red abdomens.

Flavous Nomad Bee
Nomada flava

DESCRIPTION Wing length: female 10mm, male 10mm. Females (left) have orange
eyes and antennae, four orange stripes on the thorax, orange scutellum, first
abdominal segment is black and orange, the rest are mainly yellow with black and
orange cross-bands. Males (below) have darker antennae, greenish eyes, yellow
mandibles and parts of the face and a mainly black thorax.

WHERE TO LOOK A common nomad bee of woodland and a range of open habitats.
Visits spring-flowering shrubs, Cow Parsley, Greater
Stitchwort, Bluebell and Wood Spurge.
A cleptoparasite, the female
lays her eggs in the nests of
the Chocolate Mining Bee
Andrena scotica (see p.27).

WHEN TO LOOK Late March–June.

SIMILAR SPECIES

Males are almost identical in
appearance to **Panzer's Mining
Bee *Nomada panzeri*** males.

Little Nomad Bee
Nomada flavoguttata

DESCRIPTION Wing length: female 6.5mm, male 6.5mm. Females (left and below) have a black thorax with red lines and red tubercles on the scutellum, abdomen is red with black cross-bands and a small yellow spot on the sides. Males have an entirely black thorax and large yellow marks on the sides of the abdomen.

WHERE TO LOOK Widespread and found in a great variety of habitats. Visits spring-flowering shrubs, dandelions and other composites, umbellifers (carrot family), crucifers (cabbage family) and Germander Speedwell. A cleptoparasite, the female lays her eggs in the nests of the Common Mini-miner *Andrena minutula* (see p.23).

WHEN TO LOOK Late March–June, June–September.

Painted Nomad Bee
Nomada fucata

DESCRIPTION Wing length: female 8.5mm, male 9mm. Females (left) have orange antennae and brown eyes, thorax is black with prominent yellow markings, the first abdominal segment is orange, the second partly orange and the rest have yellow bands. Males (below) have black and orange antennae and green eyes, otherwise similarly marked.

WHERE TO LOOK Found in a variety of habitats, especially chalk downland and old quarries, such as BBOWT's Dry Sandford Pit and Hitchcopse Pit (both Oxon). Visits spring-flowering shrubs, buttercups, cinquefoils and composites (daisy family). A cleptoparasite, the female lays her eggs in the nests of the Yellow-legged Mining Bee *Andrena flavipes* (see p.17).

WHEN TO LOOK April–June, July–August.

52

Gooden's Nomad Bee
Nomada goodeniana

DESCRIPTION Wing length: female 10mm, male 8.5mm. Females (left) have orange antennae and legs, yellow and orange markings on face, a black thorax with yellow markings and the abdomen has yellow bands on a black background. Males (below) are similar but have black and orange antennae and more extensive yellow on the face.

WHERE TO LOOK Common and widespread and found in a variety of open and wooded habitats. Visits spring-flowering shrubs, yellow composites such as dandelions, Cow Parsley, Greater Stitchwort, buttercups and forget-me-nots. A cleptoparasite, the female lays her eggs in the nests of the Buffish Mining Bee *Andrena nigroaenea* (see p.23), Grey-patched Mining Bee *Andrena nitida* (see p.25) and Chocolate Mining Bee *Andrena scotica* (see p.27).

WHEN TO LOOK April–June.

Lathbury's Nomad Bee
Nomada lathburiana

DESCRIPTION Wing length: female 9mm, male 9mm. Females (left) have orange antennae and orange markings on the face, is black thorax with reddish hair and yellow markings and the abdomen has a rusty-red first segment and yellow bands with variable red margins on a black background on the rest. Males (below) are similar but have black and orange antennae and paler body hair.

WHERE TO LOOK Found on heathland, sandy paths and hillsides with Gorse. Visits Gorse and spring-flowering shrubs, dandelions and Germander Speedwell. A cleptoparasite, the female lays her eggs in the nests of Ashy Mining Bee *Andrena cineraria* (see p.15).

WHEN TO LOOK April–June.

Early Nomad Bee
Nomada leucophthalma

DESCRIPTION Wing length: female 9mm, male 8.5mm. Females (left) have a black face, dark antennae with orange tips, black thorax with rusty-red markings and the abdomen has a rusty-red and black first segment, the next two segments are yellow and red on black and the rest yellow on a black background. Males (below) are similar but have very dark antennae, yellow mandibles and an entirely black thorax.

WHERE TO LOOK Found in heathy woodland, scrub and heathland, such as BBOWT's Bowdowns Woods and Greenham Common (both Berks). Visits willows, bilberry, Barren Strawberry, dandelions and forget-me-nots. A cleptoparasite, the female lays her eggs in the nests of Clarke's Mining Bee *Andrena clarkella* (see p.15) and Large Sallow Mining Bee *Andrena apicata*.

WHEN TO LOOK March–mid-May.

Marsham's Nomad Bee
Nomada marshamella

DESCRIPTION Wing length: female 9.5mm, male 9.5mm. Females (left) have orange antennae, orange marks on lower face and beside the eyes, black thorax with yellow marks and the abdomen is black with yellow bands divided centrally. Males (below) are similar but have orange antennae with some black, a yellow lower face and a black thorax that can have smaller yellow marks but is often entirely black.

WHERE TO LOOK Found in open and wooded habitats. Visits a wide variety of flowers and shrubs. A cleptoparasite, the female lays her eggs in the nests of Chocolate Mining Bee *Andrena scotica* (see p.27).

WHEN TO LOOK April–June.

Black-horned Nomad Bee
Nomada rufipes

DESCRIPTION Wing length: female 7mm, male 7mm. Females (left and below) have dark antennae and red markings on the face, a black thorax with yellow markings and the abdomen has yellow divided bands with some red but some have no red at all. Males are similar but have a yellow lower face.

WHERE TO LOOK Uncommon in our area where it is found on heathland, such as BBOWT's Greenham and Crookham Commons (Berks). Visits Heather (Ling), ragworts and thistles. A cleptoparasite, the female lays her eggs in the nests of Heather Mining Bee *Andrena fuscipes* (see p.19) and Grey-banded Mining Bee *Andrena denticulata*.

WHEN TO LOOK July–September.

Black-thighed Epeolus
Epeolus variegatus

DESCRIPTION Wing length: female 6.5mm, male 6.5mm. Females (left and below) have a black face with red mandibles and red-brown eyes, orange markings on the thorax and a white area beside each wing, a black abdomen with paired white bars and red legs that are partially black. Males are similar.

WHERE TO LOOK Rare in our area where it is found in heathy areas and areas with light soils. Visits Common Fleabane, Common Ragwort and heathers. A cleptoparasite, the female lays her eggs in the nests of Davies' Colletes *Colletes daviesanus* (see p.5).

WHEN TO LOOK July–September.

SIMILAR SPECIES

The much rarer **Red-thighed Epeolus *Epeolus cruciger***, a heathland species, is similar but the legs are almost entirely red.

58

Hairy-footed Flower Bee
Anthophora plumipes

DESCRIPTION Wing length: female 11mm, male 11mm. Females (below) are black except for hind tibia which has orange pollen collecting hairs. Males (left) are often mistaken for small carder bumblebees and are mainly ginger-brown with a yellow area on the face and have long hairs on the mid-tibia, giving the bee its common name. Both sexes have very long tongues and are often seen hovering with tongue extended by Lungwort and other garden flowers.

WHERE TO LOOK Common and widespread in gardens, woodland rides and along hedges. Visits Lungwort, Primrose, dead-nettles and other labiates. Nests in walls, 'bee hotels' and vertical faces in old quarries.

WHEN TO LOOK March–May (males), March–June (females).

CLEPTOPARASITE Common Mourning Bee *Melecta albifrons* (see p.61).

Four-banded Flower Bee
Anthophora quadrimaculata

DESCRIPTION Wing length: female 8.5mm, male 8.5mm. Females (below) have bluish-grey eyes, a dark face, brown hair on body fading to greyish with pale bands on the abdomen. Males (left) have bluish-grey eyes, a pale yellow face, brown hair on thorax and more prominent abdominal bands.

WHERE TO LOOK A rare species in our area where it is found mainly in gardens. Visits lavenders, catmints and other blue/mauve labiates and mauve Alliums in gardens, and Black Horehound and dead-nettles in semi-natural habitats. Nests in walls and 'bee hotels'.

WHEN TO LOOK June–August.

Common Mourning Bee
Melecta albifrons

look out for

DESCRIPTION Wing length: female 11.5mm, male 11.5mm. Females (left and below) have black hair on face, pale greyish-brown hair on upper head and thorax, whitish hair under the wings, a black abdomen with a row of white spots along each side and a white hair patch at the centre of the mid and hind tibia. Fully black individuals are sometimes seen. Males are similar.

WHERE TO LOOK Any habitat where its host, the Hairy-footed Flower Bee *Anthophora plumipes* is found, including gardens. Visits spring-flowering shrubs, dandelions, Ground-ivy and garden plants such as Wallflower. One particularly good site to see this bee is the Roman villa at East End, near Witney (Oxon). A cleptoparasite, the female lays her eggs in the nests of Hairy-footed Flower Bee (see p.59).

WHEN TO LOOK Mid-March– early June.

Garden Bumblebee
Bombus hortorum

DESCRIPTION Wing length: queen 16mm, worker 13mm, male 14mm. Queens (below), workers and males (left) have a similar colour pattern with a yellow band on the collar, the scutellum and the first two abdominal segments, and a white tail. The tongue is long.

WHERE TO LOOK Widespread and found in gardens, parkland and woodland rides. Visits flowers with a deep corolla, such as labiates (dead-nettle family), Primrose, honeysuckles, clovers and bindweeds. Nests in holes in the ground, including those made by small mammals, and in decaying plant material.

WHEN TO LOOK April–September.

CLEPTOPARASITE Barbut's Cuckoo Bumblebee *Bombus barbutellus*.

SIMILAR SPECIES

The rarer **Large Garden Bumblebee** *Bombus ruderatus* has short and even hair on the thorax. The queen is larger with a wing length of 18mm.

Tree Bumblebee
Bombus hypnorum

DESCRIPTION Wing length: queen 15mm, worker 11mm, male 13mm. Queens and workers (left) have bright ginger-brown hair of thorax and a black abdomen with a white tail. Males often have ginger-brown hair on the first two abdominal sections.

WHERE TO LOOK This bumblebee was first seen in Britain in 2001, and is now widespread in England and Wales. Locally it is fairly common where it is found in woodland, scrubby grassland and gardens. Visits cotoneasters, willows, brambles, roses, comfreys and Oil-seed Rape. Nests in abandoned bird boxes, holes in trees, walls and cliffs in old quarries, and are quite large with over 100 workers.

WHEN TO LOOK April–August.

SIMILAR SPECIES
The ginger-coloured carder bumblebees do not have the black abdomen.

Red-tailed Bumblebee
Bombus lapidarius

DESCRIPTION Wing length: queen 17mm, worker 12mm, male 12mm. Queens and workers (left) are black with a red tail, males (below) have yellow hairs on face, a yellow collar extending round the underside, yellow hairs on back of thorax and a red tail.

WHERE TO LOOK Very common. Found in gardens, grassland, woodland rides, hedgerows and heathland. Visits willows, Blackthorn, Gorse, dandelions, Oil-seed Rape, thistles, knapweeds and other composites, clovers and bird's-foot-trefoils. Nests underground with colonies of up to 300 workers.

WHEN TO LOOK April–October.

LEPTOPARASITE Hill Cuckoo Bumblebee *Bombus rupestris* (see p.69).

SIMILAR SPECIES
Hill Cuckoo Bumblebee
Bombus rupestris (see p.69).

White-tailed Bumblebee
Bombus lucorum

DESCRIPTION Wing length: queen 16mm, worker 12mm, male 14mm. Queens (left) and workers have two bright yellow bands and a white tail, males (below) have yellow hair on face and top of head.

WHERE TO LOOK Common and found in gardens, farmland, woodland rides and heathland. Visits willows, Blackthorn, Wild Cherry, thistles, knapweeds, brambles, Teasel, Buddleia, Viper's-bugloss, heathers, clovers and umbellifers (carrot family). Nests underground, often in rodent burrows. Colonies can be large with over 200 workers.

WHEN TO LOOK March–October.

LEPTOPARASITE Gypsy Cuckoo Bumblebee *Bombus bohemicus*.

SIMILAR SPECIES

Buff-tailed Bumblebee *Bombus terrestris* (see p.67) has a dirty white to pale buff tip to the abdomen.

Common Carder Bumblebee
Bombus pascuorum

DESCRIPTION Wing length: queen 13mm, worker 10mm, male 12mm. Queens (left) and workers (below) have ginger-bown hairs on thorax, fading to sandy brown in older bees, ginger hairs on abdomen with varying amounts of black hairs giving them a stripy look. Males have longer antennae.

WHERE TO LOOK Common, found in gardens, woodland rides, grassland, hedgerows and verges. Visits willows, legumes (vetch family), composites (daisy family), labiates (dead-nettle family), brambles, Foxglove, scabiouses and teasels. Nests above ground amongst moss and leaf litter which is carded into a loose ball.

WHEN TO LOOK March–November.

LEPTOPARASITE Field Cuckoo Bumblebee *Bombus campestris*.

SIMILAR SPECIES

Tree Bumblebee *Bombus hypnorum* (see p.63) has a white-tipped black abdomen.

Early Bumblebee
Bombus pratorum

DESCRIPTION Wing length: queen 13mm, worker 10mm, male 10mm. Queens (below) and workers have a yellow collar and a red tail. Males (left) have a broad yellow collar extending round the underside, yellow hairs on face and head, and yellow hair on the first two abdominal segments. The tongue is short.

WHERE TO LOOK Common and widespread. Found in gardens, woodland, hedgerows and grassland. Visits willows, Blackthorn, Wild Cherry, Colt's-foot, dandelions, clovers, dead-nettles, brambles, thistles, knapweeds, Devil's-bit Scabious amongst others. Nests in holes in the ground, holes in trees, old bird boxes and roof spaces. Colonies are small with no more than 100 workers.

WHEN TO LOOK March–September.

LEPTOPARASITE Forest Cuckoo Bumblebee *Bombus sylvestris* (see p.69).

Buff-tailed Bumblebee
Bombus terrestris

DESCRIPTION Wing length: queen 18mm, worker 13mm, male 14mm. Queens (below) have a narrow orange-brown collar, an orange-brown band on the abdomen and a buff tail, often peachy-orange where the black meets the buff-white tail. Workers (left) are similar but tail varies from white to buff. Males look similar to queens.

WHERE TO LOOK Very common in gardens, woodland, hedgerows and grasslands. Visits willows, Blackthorn, Gorse, Bluebell, daffodils, crocuses and garden flowers, brambles, thistles, knapweeds, daisies, scabiouses and Ivy. Nests underground in old rodent burrows. Colonies can be large with over 500 workers.

WHEN TO LOOK February–October.

LEPTOPARASITE Vestal Cuckoo Bumblebee *Bombus vestalis* (see p.71).

SIMILAR SPECIES

White-tailed Bumblebee
Bombus lucorum (see p.65) has a pure white tip to the abdomen.
Vestal Cuckoo Bumblebee
Bombus vestalis (see p.71).

Hill Cuckoo Bumblebee
Bombus rupestris

DESCRIPTION Wing length: female 19mm, male 14mm. Females (left) are black with a red tail and dark brown wings, occasionally they can have a yellow collar. Males (below) are similar but have variable pale bands on thorax and abdomen.

WHERE TO LOOK Once scarce, now increasing and found in a wide range of habitats similar to those of its host the Red-tailed Bumblebee *Bombus lapidarius*. Visits dandelions, comfreys, Oil-seed Rape, knapweeds, thistles, Viper's-bugloss, Teasel, brambles, ragworts and scabiouses. A cleptoparasite, the female lays her eggs in the nests of Red-tailed Bumblebee (see p.63).

WHEN TO LOOK May–September.

SIMILAR SPECIES

Red-tailed Bumblebee
Bombus lapidarius (see p.63).

Forest Cuckoo Bumblebee
Bombus sylvestris

DESCRIPTION Wing length: female 15mm, male 13mm. Females (left) have a wide yellow collar and a white tail. Males (below) have a white tail with a red tip, yellow hair on top of head and on the front of abdomen.

WHERE TO LOOK Widespread. Found in gardens, woodland rides, hedgerows and heathland. Visits willows, Blackthorn, dandelions, clovers, dead-nettles, bramble, thistles, Viper's-bugloss and Devil's-bit Scabious. A cleptoparasite, the female lays her eggs in the nests of Early Bumblebee *Bombus pratorum* (see p.67).

WHEN TO LOOK March–September.

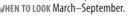

Vestal Cuckoo Bumblebee
Bombus vestalis

DESCRIPTION Wing length: female 18mm, male 14mm. Females (left and below) have an orange-yellow collar and a lemon-yellow flash between the white tail and black of the abdomen. Males are similar but have longer antennae.

WHERE TO LOOK Common and widespread. Found in gardens and in open and wooded habitats. Visits willows, Blackthorn, Wild Cherry, dandelions, dead-nettles, Ground-ivy, thistles, burdocks, Teasel, brambles and a wide range of garden plants. A cleptoparasite, the female lays her eggs in the nests of Buff-tailed Bumblebee *Bombus terrestris* (see p.67).

WHEN TO LOOK April—August, males from May.

SIMILAR SPECIES

Buff-tailed Bumblebee
Bombus terrestris (see p.67).

Honey Bee
Apis mellifera

DESCRIPTION Wing length: queen 11mm (body length: 16mm), worker 10mm, male 12mm. Queens are large, workers (left) have a heart-shaped face, black hairs on top of head, pale brown hairs on thorax and first two abdominal segments, which can be orange but are often dark as the rest of the abdomen, and there are flattened white hairs on the margins of the other abdominal segments. Hind tibia is shiny and triangular and fringed with hairs forming a pollen basket. Males, or drones, (below) are broader than workers and have large eyes that meet at the top of the head.

WHERE TO LOOK Common and widespread. Found in mosts habitats. Visits a wide variety of flowering trees, shrubs and flowers. Nests are mostly in artificial hives, but feral colonies can be found in hollow trees.

WHEN TO LOOK Any time of year when weather is suitable.

Species index

Photographers' credits